THIS BOOK BELONGS TO:

Golden Age Press

VISIT US ONLINE:
WWW.GOLDENAGEPRESS.COM

© 2022 Barbara House / BGH Publishing
Published by Golden Age Press (goldenagepress.com),
an imprint of BGH Publishing (bghpublishing.com). All Rights Reserved.

ISBN: 978-1-955421-98-0
Illustrated by: Roslen Roy Mack
Book Design & Editing: Barbara House

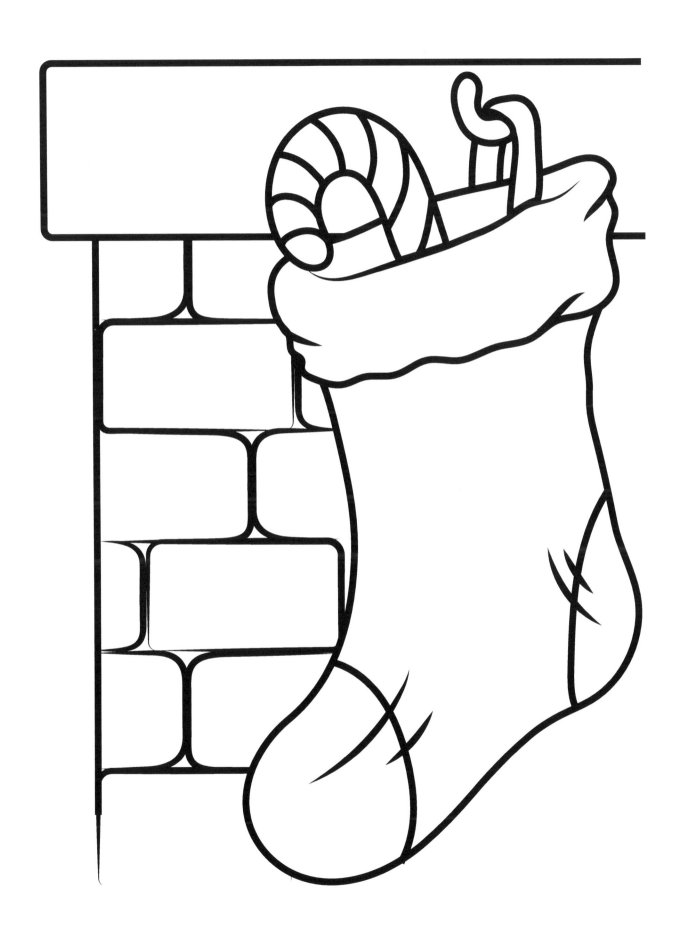

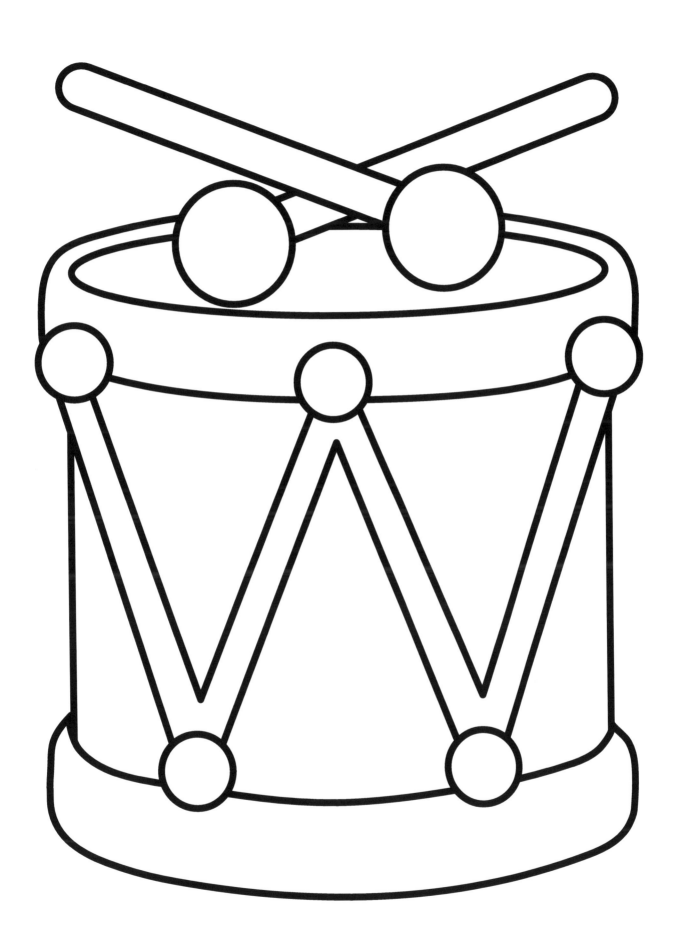

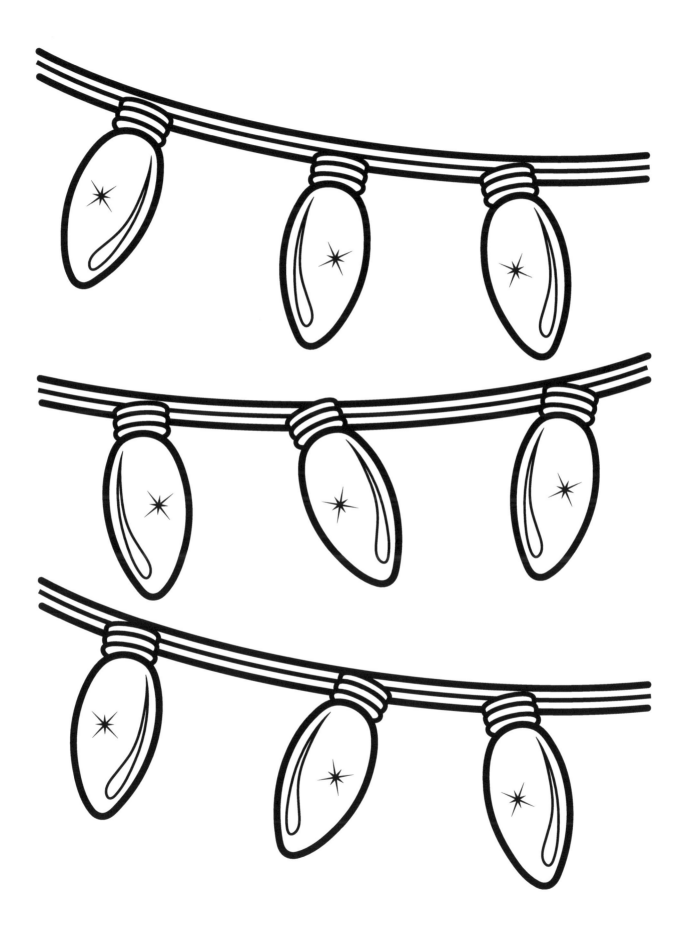

EASTER
Coloring Book for Kids

Made in the USA
Middletown, DE
04 January 2024

47182336R00035